*S...*
*Dam...*
*Signed the Rubens*
*Again*

# thelwell

# Some Damn Fool's Signed the Rubens Again

METHUEN

*First published in 1982*
*This paperback edition first published in 1984*
*by Methuen London Ltd*
*11 New Fetter Lane, London EC4P 4EE*
*© 1982 Norman Thelwell*
*ISBN 0 413 54880 5*
*Printed in Great Britain by*
*Cox & Wyman Ltd, Reading*

# Contents

A number of the cartoons in this book originally appeared in *Punch* or the *Tatler*.

# The Stately Homes

'We can't afford to maintain the place any longer. We'll *have* to throw it open to the public.'

'How long do you think we could hold out
against a wealth tax?'

'Hello! We've got squatters in the East Wing again.'

'It came unscathed through the Civil War
but succumbed to traffic vibration.'

'And then again there's the constant threat of death duties.'

'*Please* Henry! You've renounced your title.
Isn't that enough.'

'If we don't sell some of our surplus coal stocks soon, we'll
have to consider throwing the place open to the public.'

'Get a move on! I'm only a life peer.'

'In my opinion, your Grace, they're either Bronze Age,
Roman or Pop Festival Era.'

'What date do we open to the public.'

# Visitors' View

'We don't open to the public for another three weeks.'

'. . . and this is the present duke . . .'

'The original Norman keep was destroyed in 1971
to build the car park.'

'It's not as grand as this of course, but if you're ever in
Salford, your Ladyship . . .'

'It's all a front. They're still watching black and white.'

'Excuse me! Do we have to serve ourselves?'

'That's my favourite – our one hundred thousandth visitor.'

'It was a damn silly place to put the cafeteria.'

'. . . and this one was built by the ninth Earl
for his holiday pictures.'

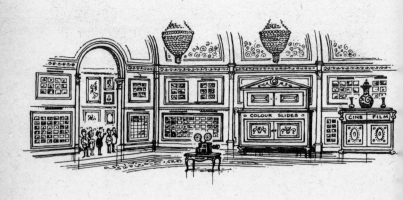

'He's come to apologise about your beautiful vase.'

'Hello! the death duties have been paid off.'

'I think she wants us to tell Women's Lib.'

'She knows perfectly well we're not open to the public.'

'Thank you for having us.'

'The story goes that the fourteenth Earl was shut in the tower
when the crowds drove him mad.'

'My family never forgave me for renouncing the title.'

'Excuse me! Is this anybody's seat?'

# Animal Crackers

'You rang, Sir?'

'Hello! You've left the gate open in the Safari Park again.'

'I've just had the feed bill – we'll have to sell
another Rubens.'

'A marvellous Christmas party I *must* say –
digging out ruddy lions.'

40

'Oh, for heaven's sake take him to see the rats
in the dungeons.'

'If we're going to have a decent hippo pool, Mildred,
the house will have to go.'

'As a matter of fact, one of the visitors got him
with an E type Jag.'

'Get rid of your leopard skin coat if you wish but keep your
hands off my trophies.'

'It could make the lions redundant.'

'I don't think much of the new game warden you took on.'

'We can never catch the visitors at it, m'Lud.'

'In the winter it's difficult to keep the wolf from the door.'

# Ticket to Ride

'Will there be any extra charge, your Grace?'

'I shudder to think of what they'll be like at their coming-out parties.'

'You are *not* going to the meet in the horse-box.
The walk will do you good.'

'How many times have I told you about hunting
out of season?'

'If there's one thing I hate about meets . . .'

'Charles! Did you ask anyone to meet you
here this morning?'

'He's asked for political asylum.'

'You never hear anything about testing *their* breath.'

'For the last time! I will not have him inside this house until you've done your homework.'

'Sandra's pony's broken a leg.'

'Put that gear back in the attic. I will *not* have you
showing off to the visitors.'

# *Roll up! Roll up!*

'Please, Henry! Please! *Not* through the family vault.'

'That does it, Mildred! No more crayons
in the souvenir shop.'

'Alright! Come on down and you can have another go
on the roundabouts.'

'They've got "Coronation Street" on the telly.'

'Of course, it was never intended for this sort of traffic.'

'I still say it was a damn silly place to put a ferris wheel.'

'Our rivals started the rumour that he's the ghost of a visitor poisoned by the bangers in the cafeteria.'

'This'll shake the Duke of Bedford! We picked up fifty-six tons more litter than he did last season.'

'Henry! Please! They're our bread and butter.'

# Living Like a Lord

'. . . and get your hair cut! You're a disgrace to the family.'

'That will be the sixth time this year that his mother-in-law's portrait has had to be restored.'

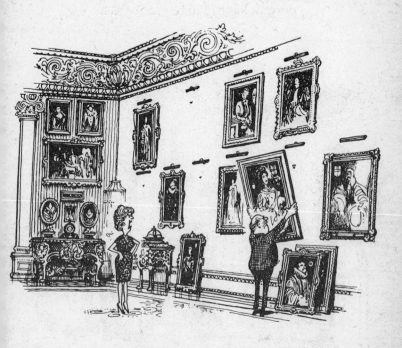

'I notice it's always my relations you reluctantly sacrifice for
tax purposes.'

'Have you had those hounds in the bedroom again?'

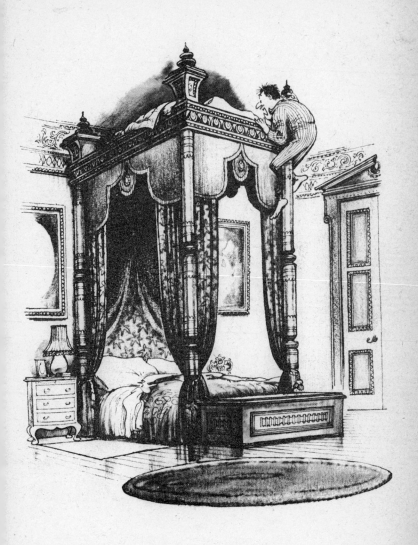

'For heaven's sake, Anthia, I've said I'm sorry.'

'The butler did it!'

'At the last minute he decided to be cremated.'

'Hold it! Hold it! You've forgotten to put the cat out.'

'Standards, banners, flags! I *hate* wash day.'

'Buck up Benson, or you'll find yourself in the snack bar!'

'Shall I start with the Black Prince's monocle or the
moustache on the Dowager Duchess?'

'Excuse me, Madame. Is this the room you want decorating?'

'That wine should be chilled, Benson. Stand it by the door
for a few minutes.'

'I can remember the time when you could be pretty sure the butler had done it.'

'I love it when the visitors have all gone for the season – having
the place to ourselves again.'

'I see F.C. of Tooting Bec was with us again this year.'

'I'm afraid the squatters have moved in, my Lord.'

'Money can't buy them happiness.'

'Will you be dusting the place for finger-prints?'

'It's nothing serious, doctor. I'm just not feeling superior,
that's all.'

'You've had all winter to get ready.'

'Great Heavens, Cynthia! We must have overslept.'

'The whole place needs redecorating.'